The Promised Land
An Old Testament Activity Book

Linda Robinson Whited

Illustrated by Robert S. Jones

Scripture quotations in this publication are from the New Revised Standard Version of the Bible, copyright © 1989 by the Division of Christian Education of the National Council of the Churches of Christ in the United States of America, and are used by permission.

ISBN 0-687-08191-2

Abingdon Press

MANUFACTURED IN THE UNITED STATED OF AMERICA

99 00 01 02 03 04 05 06 07 08 - 10 9 8 7 6 5 4 3 2 1

| 2000 B.C. | | | | | 1500 B.C. | | | | | 1250 B.C. |

God Promises Abraham a New Land · Isaac · Jacob · Joseph · Abraham's Descendants in Egypt · Moses in Egypt · Moses in Midian · God Calls Moses · Plagues in Egypt · The Passover

Go from your country...to the land that I will show you... To your offspring I will give this land.

(Genesis 12:1, 7)

Did You Know?
Abraham was a nomad. Nomads wander from place to place, looking for a place where their flocks can have grass to eat and fresh water to drink.

God made a covenant, a special promise, with Abraham. Find God's covenant in the letters.

(**Hint**: OT stands for Old Testament, the part of the Bible where Abraham's story is found. Cross out the OT's, and then write the words from Genesis 12:2 and Genesis 17:7 on the lines.)

_____

_____

_____

_____

_____

_____

_____

IOT WIOTLL MAOTKEOT OOTF YOOTUOT AOT GREOTAOTT NAOTTIOTOOTN, AOTND IOT WIOTLL BLEOTSS YOOTUOT, AOTND MAOTKEOT YOOTUOTR NAOTMEOT GREOTAOTT, SOOT THAOTT YOOTUOT WIOTLL BEOT AOT BLEOTSSIOTNG... IOT WIOTLL EOTSTAOTBLIOTSH MY COOTVEOTNAOTNT BEOTTWEOTEOTN MEOT AOTND YOOTUOT, AOTND YOOTUOTR OOTFFSPRIOTNG AOTFTEOTR YOOTUOT.

Genesis 12:2; 17:7

1200 B.C.

| God Frees the Israelites | Surviving the Wilderness | Ten Commandments | Worship in the Wilderness | Moses Sees the Promised Land | Joshua Leads God's People | The Covenant Is Renewed | Living in the Promised Land |

Color the path through the maze to find the name of the new land God promised to Abraham's family. You can pick up the six letters in the name of the land as you pass through them.

The Promised Land is called ____ ____ ____ ____ ____ ____ .

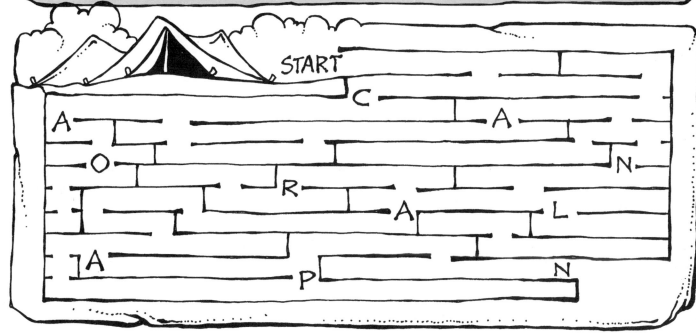

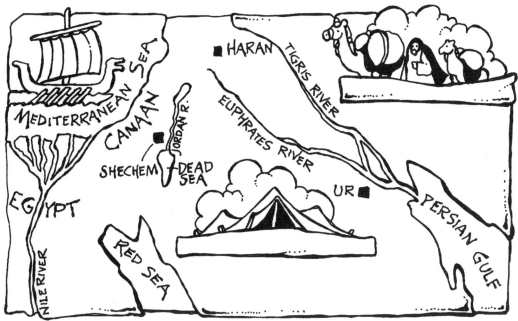

Color the map of Abraham's journey. Use green for grassy areas, brown for mountains, and yellow for desert. Then trace the route Abraham's family took from Ur to Haran and then to Canaan.

More than four thousand years ago, God called Abraham to travel to a new land, where God would begin a great nation. So Abraham and his wife, Sarah, trusting God's promise, set out to go to …

The Promised Land.

Is anything too wonderful for the LORD?... Sarah shall have a son. (Genesis 18:14*a*)

Did You Know?
Abraham had a son named Ishmael. In ancient times a woman who had no children could give her husband a second wife. The child who was born would belong to the first wife. Fourteen years before Isaac was born, Sarah gave Abraham a second wife who gave birth to a son. When Isaac was born, though, Sarah became jealous of Ishmael and his mother Hagar. She demanded that Abraham send Ishmael and his mother away. Read about what happened to Ishmael and Hagar in Genesis 21:8-21.

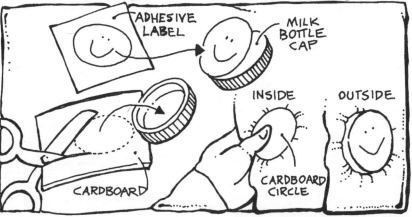

1. Cut a circle the size of a milk bottle cap from a plain self-adhesive label. (Use plain paper and a glue stick if necessary.)
2. Draw a happy face on the circle.
3. Stick the happy face to the top of a milk bottle cap.
4. Cut a second circle from cardboard. Be sure this circle will fit snugly on the inside of the bottle cap.
5. To wear your button, hold the happy face on the outside of your shirt and then push the cardboard circle into the cap from the underside of your shirt.

When you wear your happy face button, remember the happiness that Abraham and Sarah felt when Isaac was born according to God's promise!

1200 B.C.

| God Frees the Israelites | Surviving the Wilderness | Ten Commandments | Worship in the Wilderness | Moses Sees the Promised Land | Joshua Leads God's People | The Covenant Is Renewed | Living in the Promised Land |

A **blessing** is a gift of love that brings happiness to others. God promised that all the families of the earth would be blessed because of Abraham's covenant with God. Read Galatians 3:29 to find out how you are blessed by Abraham's faith even if you are not one of his many descendants.

Read the story of visitors who told Abraham and Sarah about Isaac's birth in Genesis 18:1-15.

For each statement that is true, fill in all the T's.
For each statement that is false, fill in all the F's.

Then read the word that your answer spells to discover the meaning of Isaac's name.

1. God promised that Abraham and Sarah would have a child, and then later many descendants.

2. When Abraham heard that he would be a father when he was 100 years old, he laughed.

3. Abraham and Sarah always trusted God, never doubting that God would give them a son.

4. When visitors arrived, Abraham was reluctant to invite them into his home.

5. When Sarah heard the visitors say that she would have a baby after she was 90 years old, she laughed.

6. When Isaac was born, Sarah became jealous of Hagar's son, Ishmael.

7. Abraham continued to take care of Ishmael and his mother, Hagar, even after Isaac was born.

8. God kept the promise to give Abraham many descendants through Isaac.

1.	T	F	F	F	F
	T	F	F	F	F
	T	F	F	F	F
	T	F	F	F	F
	T	T	T	T	T

2.	T	T	T	T	T
	T	F	F	F	T
	T	T	T	T	T
	T	F	F	F	T
	T	F	F	F	T

3.	F	T	T	T	T
	F	T	T	T	T
	F	T	T	T	T
	F	T	T	T	T
	F	F	F	F	F

4.	F	F	F	F	F
	F	T	T	T	T
	F	T	F	F	F
	F	T	T	T	F
	F	F	F	F	F

5.	T	F	F	F	T
	T	F	F	F	T
	T	T	T	T	T
	T	F	F	F	T
	T	F	F	F	T

6.	T	T	T	T	T
	F	F	T	F	F
	F	F	T	F	F
	F	F	T	F	F
	F	F	T	F	F

7.	F	F	F	F	F
	F	T	T	T	T
	F	F	F	T	T
	F	T	T	T	T
	F	F	F	F	F

8.	T	T	T	T	T
	T	F	F	F	T
	T	F	T	T	F
	T	F	F	F	F
	T	F	F	F	T

Isaac means _____ _____ _____ _____ _____ _____ _____ _____ _____ .

By the time Abraham was ninety-nine years old and Sarah was eighty-nine, they had given up on having a child as God had promised. When visitors told them that a son would be born by the next year, each of them laughed. It seemed impossible! But, when Abraham was one hundred and Sarah was ninety, Isaac was born in …

The Promised Land.

2000 B.C. ———————————— 1500 B.C. ———————————— 1250 B.C.

| God Promises Abraham a New Land | Isaac | **Jacob** | Joseph | Abraham's Descendants in Egypt | Moses in Egypt | Moses in Midian | God Calls Moses | Plagues in Egypt | The Passover |

Know that I am with you and will keep you wherever you go, and will bring you back to this land.

(Genesis 28:15)

Did You Know?

The birthright was a special benefit for a firstborn son in Bible times. It meant that the oldest son inherited most of the family's property and also carried on the family's name. Esau was unwise enough to give his birthright away to Jacob for a simple bowl of soup!

What's in a Name?

Bible names often have special meaning, a symbol of a new relationship with God. Match these names with their possible meanings. If you need help, look up the Bible references. Check the footnotes too!

(**Note**: There is no clue for the meaning of the name Sarah. Find it by discovering what is left when the others have been correctly matched.)

Lentil Stew

2 cups dried lentils
8 cups water
1/2 cup each of chopped onion, celery, carrots, and tomatoes
1 cup chopped meat
Salt and pepper to taste

Wash and sort the lentils. Add the lentils to a large pot with the water, onions, celery, and carrots. Cook until the lentils are tender. Then add the tomatoes, meat, and seasonings. Serve steaming hot with chunks of bread.

Abraham (Genesis 17:5)   laughter

Sarah (Genesis 17:15)   the hairy one, also nicknamed Red

Isaac (Genesis 21:6)   one who strives with God

Esau (Genesis 25:25, 30)   princess

Jacob (Genesis 25:26)   ancestor of many nations

Israel (Genesis 32:28)   one who takes another by the heel

1200 B.C.

God Frees the Israelites • Surviving the Wilderness • Ten Commandments • Worship in the Wilderness • Moses Sees the Promised Land • Joshua Leads God's People • The Covenant Is Renewed • Living in the Promised Land

As Jacob left Canaan, God made a promise to him. You can read God's promise to Jacob if you follow these instructions.

Change all the **Z**'s to **O**'s.
Change all the **C**'s to **R**'s.
Change all the **X**'s to **M**'s.
Change all the **O**'s to **T**'s.
Change all the **R**'s to **E**'s.

Change all the **L**'s to **I**'s.
Change all the **J**'s to **B**'s.
Change all the **B**'s to **A**'s.
Change all the **Q**'s to **C**'s.
Change all the **A**'s to **L**'s.

Read the rest of God's promise to Jacob in your Bible in Genesis 28:13b-15.

Leave all the other letters the same.

L B X O H R A Z C D O H R G Z D Z F
I A M T H E L O R D, T H E G O D O F

B J C B H B X B N D O H R G Z D Z F
A B R A H A M A N D T H E G O D O F

L S B B Q O H R A B N D Z N W H L Q H
I S A A C. T H E L A N D O N W H I C H

Y Z U A L R L W L A A G L V R O Z Y Z U
Y O U L I E I W I L L G I V E T O Y O U

B N D O Z Y Z U C Z F F S P C L N G
A N D T O Y O U R O F F S P R I N G ...

K N Z W O H B O L W L A A J C L N G
K N O W T H A T I W I L L B R I N G ...

Y Z U J B Q K O Z O H L S A B N D
Y O U B A C K T O T H I S L A N D.

Isaac and his wife, Rebekah, had twin sons. Esau was the oldest, but Jacob convinced Esau to give up his birthright for a bowl of stew. Then later Jacob tricked his father, Isaac, into giving him the family blessing. But, even as Jacob fled from his home, God repeated the promise first made to Abraham: "I will bring you back to this land." Jacob knew that someday he would return to …

The Promised Land.

2000 B.C. ——————————————— 1500 B.C. ——————————————— 1250 B.C.

| God Promises Abraham a New Land | Isaac | Jacob | **Joseph** | Abraham's Descendants in Egypt | Moses in Egypt | Moses in Midian | God Calls Moses | Plagues in Egypt | The Passover |

The LORD was with Joseph and showed him steadfast love.
(Genesis 39:21*a*)

Did You Know?

A robe with long sleeves was not suitable for working in the fields or taking care of the sheep. It was a constant reminder to Joseph's brothers that their father loved Joseph best. One translation of the Bible even describes the robe as "a coat of many colors," which would surely have been more expensive than the robes Joseph's brothers wore as they tended the flocks. It is no wonder that Joseph's brothers were jealous.

Read the names of Joseph and his eleven brothers and one sister in Exodus 1:1-4 and Genesis 30:21. Then find the names in the word search.

The names may be written forward or backwards, up or down, across or diagonal.

```
A U J L N B E N J A L D
N E O L E J P H I O S I
A S S U N Z O V O S E L
D A E S M A E O R M E A
J O P V I L U B E P H T
P E H J A M I N U E P H
N I M A J N E B B L E P
D D I N A H J O E L U A
J A I S S S A M N R H N
D G A C H A H D R A M N
B E N J J O S E U O D Z
I S S A C H A R R J O S
```

——— 1200 B.C. ———

| God Frees the Israelites | Surviving the Wilderness | Ten Commandments | Worship in the Wilderness | Moses Sees the Promised Land | Joshua Leads God's People | The Covenant Is Renewed | Living in the Promised Land |

Some versions of the Bible call Joseph's robe a "coat of many colors." Use the Bible verses to choose the colors for Joseph's robe. (**Hint**: If a verse names more than one color, use the first color mentioned.)

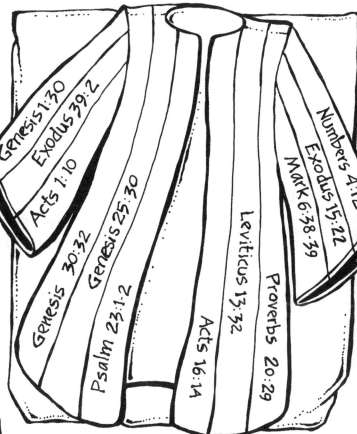

After Joseph's brothers had discovered their brother Joseph in Egypt, they had to return to their father Jacob and explain what had happened. Imagine that your are one of Joseph's brothers. What would you tell Jacob?

Jacob did return to Canaan, the land that had been promised to his family through his grandfather, Abraham. He brought with him twelve sons and one daughter. God's promise to Abraham of many descendants was beginning to be fulfilled!

But there was trouble in the family. Jacob loved his son Joseph more than his other children. When Jacob gave Joseph a beautiful robe with long sleeves, Joseph's brothers were jealous. They sold Joseph to Midianite traders who were on their way to Egypt. Little did they know that Joseph would someday save his family so that they could inherit …

The Promised Land.

2000 B.C. ———————————— 1500 B.C. ———————————— 1250 B.C.

God Promises   Isaac   Jacob   Joseph   **Abraham's**   Moses   Moses   God   Plagues   The
Abraham   **Descendants** in   in   Calls   in   Passover
a New Land   **in Egypt**   Egypt Midian Moses Egypt

Israel settled in the land of Egypt, in the region of Goshen; ... and were fruitful and multiplied exceedingly.

(Genesis 47:27)

Did You Know?

People in many parts of the world today still suffer from hunger caused by famine. Famines usually happen when there is not enough rain to make the crops grow. But famines can also be caused by insects who destroy crops and by people who destroy the land so that it will not produce food. People who live where there is famine depend on others who have plenty of food to share with them so that they can survive.

Jacob's whole family finally came to Egypt to escape starvation. Find which letter of the alphabet is missing from each line. Then read what was happening in Egypt and the the lands around it down the end of the rows.

A B C D E G H I J K L M N O P Q R S T U V W X Y Z _____
B C D E F G H I J K L M N O P Q R S T U V W X Y Z _____
A B C D E F G H I J K L N O P Q R S T U V W X Y Z _____
A B C D E F G H J K L M N O P Q R S T U V W X Y Z _____
A B C D E F G H I J K L M O P Q R S T U V W X Y Z _____
A B C D F G H I J K L M N O P Q R S T U V W X Y Z _____

1200 B.C.

| God Frees the Israelites | Surviving the Wilderness | Ten Commandments | Worship in the Wilderness | Moses Sees the Promised Land | Joshua Leads God's People | The Covenant Is Renewed | Living in the Promised Lan |

Find the numbers hidden in the sack of grain to answer the questions. Use each number only once to answer one of the questions.

How many children were born to Joseph in Egypt? _____ (Genesis 46:27)

How many members of Jacob's family came into Egypt? _____ (Genesis 46:27)

How many years did Jacob, now called Israel, live in Egypt? _____ (Genesis 47:27-28)

How old was Jacob when he died? _____ (Genesis 47:27-28)

How long did Joseph live? _____ (Genesis 50:22)

Joseph's brothers asked for Joseph's forgiveness. When do you need forgiveness? Use the letters of the word **Forgiveness** to help you name some of those times. The letter F is done to get you started.

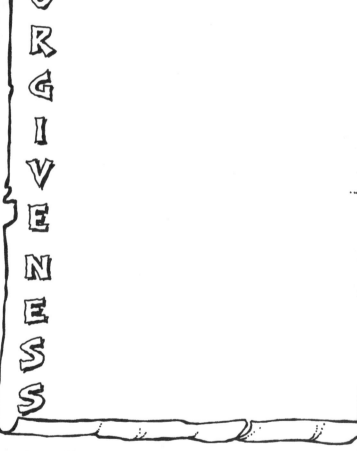

Forgot to clean my room

F
O
R
G
I
V
E
N
E
S
S

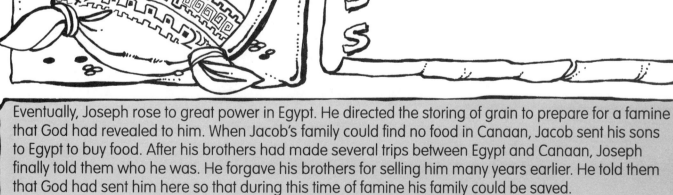

Eventually, Joseph rose to great power in Egypt. He directed the storing of grain to prepare for a famine that God had revealed to him. When Jacob's family could find no food in Canaan, Jacob sent his sons to Egypt to buy food. After his brothers had made several trips between Egypt and Canaan, Joseph finally told them who he was. He forgave his brothers for selling him many years earlier. He told them that God had sent him here so that during this time of famine his family could be saved.

Joseph sent for his father, Jacob. All of Jacob's family—seventy people—settled in the land of Goshen in Egypt. Jacob's family, the descendants promised to Abraham, were saved. But once again, they had to leave …

The Promised Land.

000 B.C.	1500 B.C.	1250 B.C.

God Promises Abraham a New Land · Isaac · Jacob · Joseph · **Abraham's Descendants in Egypt** · Moses in Egypt · Moses in Midian · God Calls Moses · Plagues in Egypt · The Passover

A new king arose over Egypt, who did not know Joseph.

(Exodus 1:8)

Did You Know?

Hebrews, Israelites, and Jews are three names used at different times to identify the nation of people who descended from Abraham. The Bible calls Abraham a Hebrew. Later God gave Jacob a new name—Israel. From that name, Abraham's descendants became known as Israelites. The names Israelites and Hebrews are often used interchangeably in the Bible. By New Testament times the name Jew was used to name people from Judah, in The Promised Land, who worshiped the God of Abraham.

1200 B.C.

| God Frees the Israelites | Surviving the Wilderness | Ten Commandments | Worship in the Wilderness | Moses Sees the Promised Land | Joshua Leads God's People | The Covenant Is Renewed | Living in the Promised Lar |

Use these word-bricks to build a wall for Pharaoh. If you do not know an answer, find and read the verse in your Bible.

1. A nomad who God promised to give many descendants in a new land. (Genesis 17:4-8)
2. The name of the land that is The Promised Land. (Genesis 12:5-7)
3. The son that God promised to Abraham and Sarah. (Genesis 21:1-3)
4. A new name given to Jacob by God. (Genesis 35:10)
5. The country to which Jacob and all his household moved during a time of famine. (Exodus 1:1)
6. Jacob's son who was already in the new country when the family arrived. His brothers threw him in a pit and then later sold him to traders passing by. (Genesis 37:23, 24, 28)
7. The Hebrews were forced to build supply cities for this ruler. (Exodus 1:11)
8. Another name used to refer to the Hebrews. (Exodus 1:12)
9. The material the Israelites added to the clay and mud to make bricks. (Exodus 5:7)
10. The promise God made to Jacob and Jacob's family was that God would be with them in these places. (Genesis 28:15a)

Jacob's and Joseph's family—the many descendants of Abraham—multiplied and grew exceedingly strong in Egypt. After many generations, though, there was a new king in Egypt. The new king did not know about what Joseph had done for Egypt. But he knew that there were too many Israelites in Egypt, and he feared them. So, he oppressed the Israelites and made them slaves. After several generations of slavery, many of the Israelites began to forget about …

The Promised Land.

...000 B.C.				1500 B.C.				1250 B.C.	
...od Promises Abraham ...a New Land	Isaac	Jacob	Joseph	Abraham's Descendants in Egypt	**Moses in Egypt**	Moses in Midian	God Calls Moses	Plagues in Egypt	The Passover

When the child [Moses] grew up, she [his mother, Jochebed] brought him to Pharaoh's daughter, and she took him as her son. (Exodus 2:10*c*)

Did You Know?

The ancient Egyptians depended on the Nile River to provide water to make life possible in the area. A powerful civilization grew up near the river. When Joseph went to Egypt, there were many artists, writers, and scientists. The Egyptians worshiped many gods. When Moses grew up in Egypt, his Israelite family were slaves who were forced to build huge cities and great statues to honor the king who made them slaves.

Hieroglyphics are the characters used in the writing of the ancient Egyptians. Moses may have studied hieroglyphics. Can you read these hieroglyphics?

____ **1.**  **A.** to fly

____ **2.**  **B.** Loaded boat

____ **3.**  **C.** Tree

____ **4.**  **D.** To see

____ **5.**  **E.** Dew, rain

____ **6.**  **F.** Night

____ **7.**  **G.** To walk

____ **8.**  **H.** Moon, month

____ **9.**  **I.** Water

____ **10.**  **J.** Agricultural land

Write your own hieroglyphic message. Make your own story figures and assign them meaning.

Moses was raised in Egypt as the son of the Pharaoh's daughter. What subjects might Moses have taken in school? Use your reading and math skills to decipher the code and find some things Moses studied.

A+2 J–2 K–6 G+6 B+7 X–5 I+11 Q+1 U+4

E+7 H–7 Z–3

T–4 F+9 H–3 R+2 N+4 V+3

H+5 N+7 W–4 K–2 A+2

H–7 R+1 X–4 O+3 N+1 R–4 K+4 P–3 Q+9

D+4 M–4 I–4 W–5 I+6 A+7 R–6 N+11 U–5 D+4 B+7 G–4 T–1

Find the names of six brave women who helped prepare Moses to answer God's call to save the people of Israel. (**Note**: One woman's name is two words.)

Two midwives—Exodus 1:15-17
Moses' mother and sister—Numbers 26:59
Moses' rescuer—Exodus 2:5
Moses' wife—Exodus 2:21

```
H S P R I M I R
S P H U A Z 'S D
D A A I J O C H
H A R O P P I Z
M I A M R R J 'S
M O O M I R A D
S S H I P U A H
E R 'S D A U G H
B E D U G T E R
J O C H E B E D
P H T P H A R A
B E E D M I R I
R R O P P I Z 'S
```

God did not forget the Israelite people who were slaves in Egypt. And God did not forget the promise to Abraham. Even while God's people suffered in slavery, God made a plan to deliver them.

Moses was born into an Israelite slave family. Moses was saved by the pharaoh's own daughter and raised in the courts of Egypt. God was preparing Moses to lead the Israelite people out of Egypt, back to …

The Promised Land.

2000 B.C. 1500 B.C. 1250 B.C.

God Promises | Isaac | Jacob | Joseph | Abraham's | Moses | **Moses** | God | Plagues | The
Abraham | | | | Descendants | in | **in** | Calls | in | Passover
a New Land | | | | in Egypt | Egypt | **Midian** | Moses | Egypt |

Moses fled from Pharaoh. He settled in the land of Midian.

(Exodus 2:15*b,c*)

Did You Know?
The Midianites were distantly related to Moses. They were descended from Midian who was the son of Abraham and his wife Keturah.

Moses had to escape from Egypt before Pharaoh found out about the Egyptian he killed. Help Moses find his way through the Egyptian pyramids to Midian. Count backward from **50** to **1**.

─── 1200 B.C. ───

| God Frees the Israelites | Surviving the Wilderness | Ten Commandments | Worship in the Wilderness | Moses Sees the Promised Land | Joshua Leads God's People | The Covenant Is Renewed | Living in the Promised Land |

Decipher the code to find words that might have helped Moses if he had been able to read from the Book of Psalms as we can today.

A B C D E F G H I J K L M N O P Q R S T U V W X Y Z

Psalm 56:3-4a

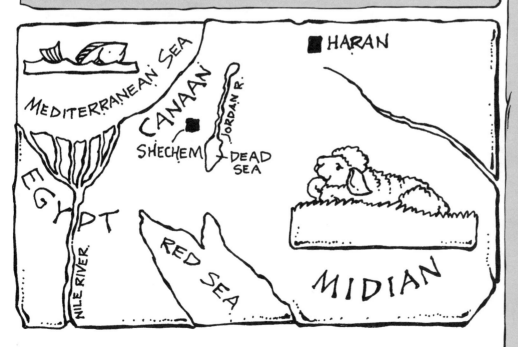

Draw a line from Egypt to Midian on the map. You can color the map. Remember that green is for grassy areas, brown is for mountains, and yellow is for desert.

One day Moses made a big mistake. When he saw an Egyptian beating an Israelite—one of his own Hebrew family—Moses acted in anger and killed the Egyptian. Fearing for his own life, Moses fled from Egypt. He hid from Pharaoh in Midian, where he married and became a shepherd. For a while it seemed that God's people would remain slaves in Egypt. More and more of the Israelites began to forget about …

The Promised Land.

2000 B.C. ——————————————— 1500 B.C. ——————————————— 1250 B.C.

| God Promises Abraham a New Land | Isaac | Jacob | Joseph | Abraham's Descendants in Egypt | Moses in Egypt | Moses in Midian | **God Calls Moses** | Plagues in Egypt | The Passover |

"Thus you shall say to the Israelites, 'The LORD, the God of your ancestors, the God of Abraham, the God of Isaac, and the God of Jacob has sent me to you.' "

(Exodus 3:15*a*)

Did You Know?
When Moses went to Midian, he married the daughter of Jethro the priest. Moses' wife was Zipporah, and their two sons were Gershom and Eliezer.

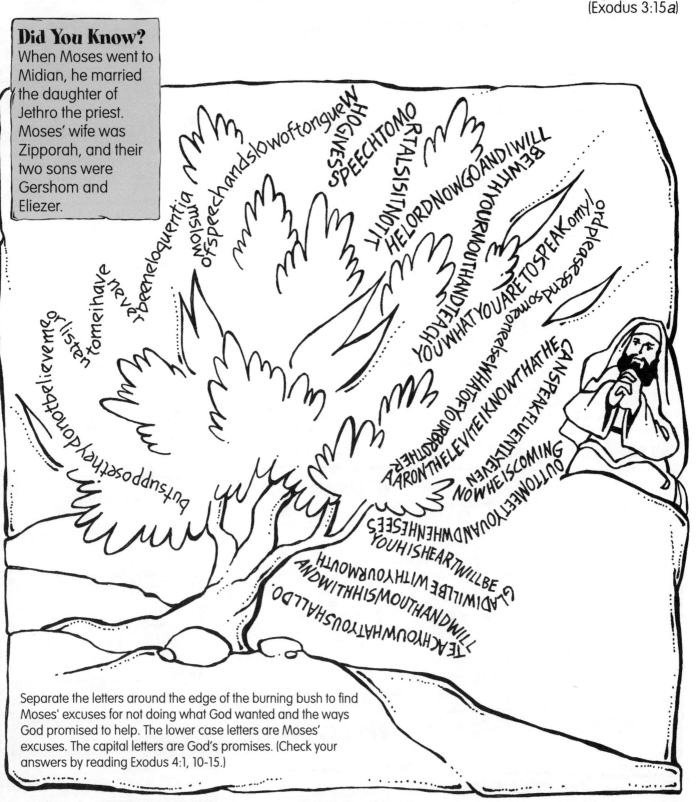

Separate the letters around the edge of the burning bush to find Moses' excuses for not doing what God wanted and the ways God promised to help. The lower case letters are Moses' excuses. The capital letters are God's promises. (Check your answers by reading Exodus 4:1, 10-15.)

1200 B.C.

| God Frees the Israelites | Surviving the Wilderness | Ten Commandments | Worship in the Wilderness | Moses Sees the Promised Land | Joshua Leads God's People | The Covenant Is Renewed | Living in the Promised Land |

Be a Poet
Write a last line for each stanza of the poem. Add more stanzas if you wish.

Moses could hardly believe his eyes,
he was filled with fright.
He turned to look and what he saw

_____.

God called to Moses
"My people suffer so,
They are slaves to Pharaoh,

_____.

Moses didn't want to make the trip,
and he quickly told God so.
"Surely there is someone else," he said,

_____.

But God wanted Moses to do the job,
So God provided a way,
"I'll send your brother Aaron,

_____.

When they said to Pharaoh,
"Let God's people go."
Pharaoh didn't care at all,

_____.

Then God stepped in,
to make Pharaoh hear.
When the people saw what God had done,

_____.

God stills helps us
with hard tasks today.
God helps us to help others,

_____.

Do I Have To?
Moses wasn't sure he was the right person for the job God was calling him to do, so Moses made excuses to try to get out of it. Sometimes we make excuses too. Match each task with an excuse we might use if we are not self-confident or if we are lazy.

Task	Excuse
Clean your room	He wants his mother, not me.
Help cook supper	It sure didn't help some of the adults I know.
Do your homework	It doesn't bother me the way it is.
Go to Sunday school	No one would eat what I fix.
Look after a younger child	The teacher shouldn't expect so much.

One day while Moses was tending his father-in-law's sheep, he saw a bush that was on fire but not being burned. When Moses turned to look, he heard God call from the bush, "Moses, you must go back to Egypt to free my people." Moses began to make excuses. Surely God did not mean to send him! God agreed to send Moses' brother Aaron with him. And God promised to be with them. Together they would confront Pharaoh. Together they would lead God's people back to the land that had been promised to their ancestor Abraham. Together they would lead God's people back to...

The Promised Land.

2000 B.C. ———————— 1500 B.C. ———————— 1250 B.C.

| God Promises Abraham a New Land | Isaac | Jacob | Joseph | Abraham's Descendants in Egypt | Moses in Egypt | Moses in Midian | God Calls Moses | **Plagues in Egypt** | The Passover |

Thus says the LORD, the God of Israel, "Let my people go … .

(Exodus 5:1)

Did You Know?

The straw the slaves mixed with mud and sand made the bricks strong. And the straw also made the bricks dry faster. In fact, when the bricks were finished, they were covered with extra straw to keep them from sticking together.

1. Cross out all the words that are used more than once.
2. Cross out all the words that have the letter W or N.
3. Cross out all the words that have exactly five letters.
4. Cross out all the words that are names of people.
5. Cross out all the words that end with the letter R.

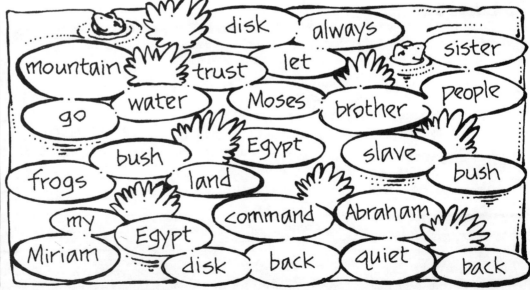

Now write the words that are left in order to find God's message to Pharaoh.

_____

1200 B.C.

| God Frees the Israelites | Surviving the Wilderness | Ten Commandments | Worship in the Wilderness | Moses Sees the Promised Land | Joshua Leads God's People | The Covenant Is Renewed | Living in the Promised Land |

When Pharaoh would not let the people go free, God sent plagues to convince him and to show God's power to the Israelite people. Name the ten plagues God sent by unscrambling each set of letters. Then match each plague with the right Bible reference.

LBODO _____   Exodus 10:13-14

RGFSO _____   Exodus 9:2-3

SGATN _____   Exodus 12:29

LFSEI _____   Exodus 7:20-21

CLESTEPENI _____   Exodus 8:17

LBSOI _____   Exodus 10:22

HLIA _____   Exodus 8:5-6

TUOLCSS _____   Exodus 8:21-24

RADNKSES _____   Exodus 9:22-26

HETDA _____   Exodus 9:10

How many frogs can you find on these pages?

FOLD PAPER PLATE IN HALF...

TRACE PATTERN HALF...

CUT ON HEAVY SOLID LINES.

OPEN PLATE, COLOR IN EYES, ETC... FOLD DOWN ARMS. FOLD LEGS UNDER, THEN FORWARD SO FROG BOUNCES ON LILY PAD.

Pharaoh did not make it easy for Moses and Aaron when they delivered God's message: "Let my people go!" Instead Pharaoh and the Egyptians endured plague after plague as God's power was shown in the land. Both the Egyptians and the Israelites saw God's mighty power. Slowly, the Israelites began to trust God once again. They began to remember the stories of their ancestors. And they began to think about what it would be like to go to the "land flowing with milk and honey" that had been promised to Abraham. They began to look forward to going to Canaan, …

The Promised Land.

2000 B.C.	1500 B.C.	1250 B.C.

| God Promises Abraham a New Land | Isaac | Jacob | Joseph | Abraham's Descendants in Egypt | Moses in Egypt | Moses in Midian | God Calls Moses | Plagues in Egypt | **The Passover** |

That very day the Lord brought the Israelites out of the land of Egypt.

(Exodus 12:51)

Did You Know?

When Jesus came to Jerusalem on the day we now celebrate as Palm Sunday, he was coming to celebrate Passover with his disciples.

Read about the preparations for the final plague in Exodus 12:1-14, 24-28. Then find a place to fill in each word that will complete the puzzle. When you finish, you will find the name of a Jewish festival that is still celebrated today to remember the night that God led the Israelite slaves out of Egypt.

God told Moses that the night of the last plague would be remembered and celebrated as the _____ month of the year for Hebrews. (Exodus 12:2)

On that night the blood of a lamb was to be put on the two _____ and lintel of the houses of the Israelites. (Exodus 12:7) Then the people in the house would share a meal of roasted _____, _____ bread, and bitter _____. (Exodus 12:8)

When the Lord passed over the houses of Israelites, the blood on the houses would be a _____, and no plague would destroy the people of Israel. (Exodus 12:13)

The Lord said that this day would be a day of _____ for the Israelites. (Exodus 12:14) It would be a day when they recall that God had passed over their houses on the night that the _____ of all others in the land of Egypt were destroyed. (Exodus 12:12)

1200 B.C.

| God Frees the Israelites | Surviving the Wilderness | Ten Commandments | Worship in the Wilderness | Moses Sees the Promised Land | Joshua Leads God's People | The Covenant Is Renewed | Living in the Promised Land |

Today Jews celebrate Passover with a meal called the Seder. The specific foods are reminders of God's great deed in freeing the Egyptian slaves.

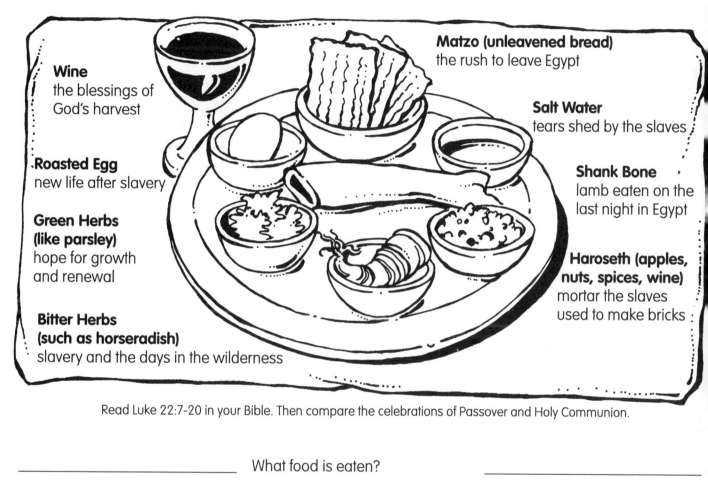

Wine
the blessings of God's harvest

Roasted Egg
new life after slavery

Green Herbs (like parsley)
hope for growth and renewal

Bitter Herbs (such as horseradish)
slavery and the days in the wilderness

Matzo (unleavened bread)
the rush to leave Egypt

Salt Water
tears shed by the slaves

Shank Bone
lamb eaten on the last night in Egypt

Haroseth (apples, nuts, spices, wine)
mortar the slaves used to make bricks

Read Luke 22:7-20 in your Bible. Then compare the celebrations of Passover and Holy Communion.

_____ What food is eaten? _____

_____ What special event does it recall? _____

_____ When is it celebrated? _____

_____ Who shares the meal? _____

_____ Why is it important? _____

God brought one last plague. At midnight, God ordered that all the firstborn of Egypt should die. But God gave instructions to save the Israelites. When they prepared a lamb for their meal that night, they were to put some of the lamb's blood on the doorways into their houses. When the plague passed through the land that night, it passed over the houses of those who had obeyed God's instructions.

God told the Israelites to remember what God had done for them this night. And they knew that they would celebrate this special meal throughout the generations. It would be a festival to the Lord that would begin when they reached …

The Promised Land.

2000 B.C. ———————————————— 1500 B.C. ———————————————— 1250 B.C.

| God Promises Abraham a New Land | Isaac | Jacob | Joseph | Abraham's Descendants in Egypt | Moses in Egypt | Moses in Midian | God Calls Moses | Plagues in Egypt | The Passover |

Do not be afraid, stand firm, and see the deliverance that the LORD will accomplish for you today.

(Exodus 14:13)

Did You Know?

An accurate translation of the Hebrew words *Red Sea is* the words *sea* and *reeds*. Since reeds do not grow around the large southern body of the Red Sea, it is likely that the Israelites crossed somewhere near the lakes at the northern points of the Red Sea, possibly near Lake Timsah where the seas were known for the reeds that grew on their banks. But no matter where the miracle of the crossing of the sea happened, we know that God made it possible.

Color the path that completes each maze from beginning to end to find the word that describes the Israelites exit from Egypt.

START AT ★... END AT ●

Find the book in your Bible that tells about the slaves leaving Egypt.

It is the Book of __ __ __ __ __ __.

1200 B.C.

| God Frees the Israelites | Surviving the Wilderness | Ten Commandments | Worship in the Wilderness | Moses Sees the Promised Land | Joshua Leads God's People | The Covenant Is Renewed | Living in the Promised Land |

Deliverance is a word often used to describe God's rescue of the Israelites from slavery. Moses is often called "the deliverer."

How many words can you make from the letters in the word **D E L I V E R A N C E**?

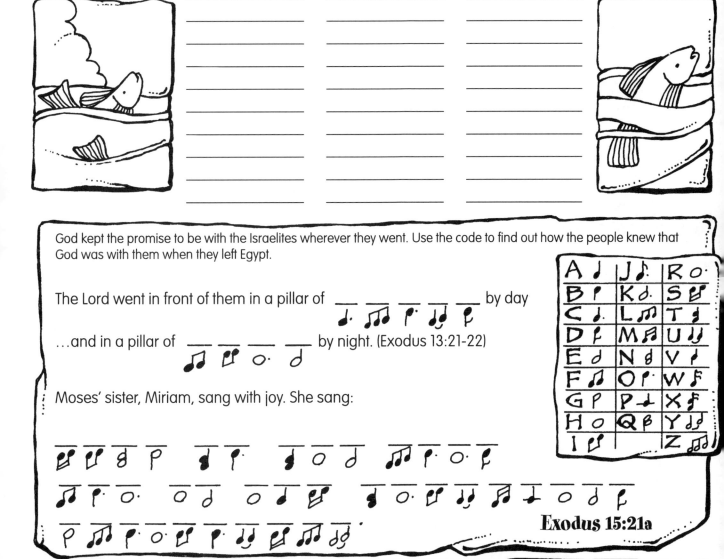

God kept the promise to be with the Israelites wherever they went. Use the code to find out how the people knew that God was with them when they left Egypt.

The Lord went in front of them in a pillar of ___ ___ ___ ___ ___ by day

…and in a pillar of ___ ___ ___ ___ by night. (Exodus 13:21-22)

Moses' sister, Miriam, sang with joy. She sang:

Exodus 15:21a

The Israelites left Egypt quickly. Soon they found themselves standing on the banks of the Red Sea. To make it worse, Pharaoh had changed his mind! His army was coming to take the people back to Egypt. The Israelites saw the Red Sea, a barrier of water that stood between them and freedom.

But the Red Sea was one more opportunity for the people to recognize God's power to save them. And God did just that! Through Moses, God opened the waters of the Red Sea and provided a way to safety for the people of Israel.

When the Israelites reached the other side of the sea, Miriam, Moses' sister, led them in a victory dance and song. Once again the people had courage. They believed that God would take them to …

The Promised Land.

2000 B.C.	1500 B.C.	1250 B.C.

God Promises Abraham a New Land	Isaac	Jacob	Joseph	Abraham's Descendants in Egypt	Moses in Egypt	Moses in Midian	God Calls Moses	Plagues in Egypt	The Passover

The Israelites ate manna for forty years, ... until they came to the border of the land of Canaan.

(Exodus 16:35)

Did You Know?
The word manna means "What is it." "What is it?" is the question the Israelites asked when they first saw the manna on the ground.

The slaves had to work hard in Egypt, but God led them back to The Promised Land. Can you go from *Work* to *Land* in four steps by changing only one letter in the word at each step.

WORK

WOR__

W__R__

___R__

LAND

Moses killed an Egyptian. But later God called Moses to *save* the Hebrew slaves. Can you go from *Kill* to *Save* in five steps?

KILL

__ILL

__IL__

___L__

___L__

SAVE

Now try a harder one. In the wilderness the Israelites needed something to drink. Moses had to find a place where there was water. Go from *Drink* to *Place* in five steps.

DRINK

_____

_____

_____

_____

PLACE

1 omer = about 2 quarts = 1/2 gallon

Read Exodus 16:16. Figure how much manna would be gathered by your family each day. Include everyone who lives in your house or eats meals with you regularly.

There are _____ people in my family. My family would gather _____ omers of manna each day. In today's measurements that would be _____ quarts or _____ gallons.

—— 1200 B.C. ——

| God Frees the Israelites | **Surviving the Wilderness** | Ten Commandments | Worship in the Wilderness | Moses Sees the Promised Land | Joshua Leads God's People | The Covenant Is Renewed | Living in the Promised Land |

Taste Manna!

1/4 cup honey
1/4 cup peanut butter
1/2 cup dry milk solids
3/4 cup graham cracker crumbs

Mix the ingredients in the order listed. Then knead the mixture with your hands. When the dough is well blended, shape it into about 12 thin wafers. The shapes can be irregular, but make them approximately 1 1/2 inches. across.

The Bible says manna wafers were like coriander seed and white or the color of gum resin. These wafers may not look like manna, but the taste of "wafers made with honey" may be similar to what the people ate in the wilderness. (Exodus 16:31)

Do you remember a line from Lord's Prayer about daily bread? Write that line here.

_____

What do you expect God to do when you say that part of the Lord's prayer?

_____

_____

_____

Only three days after the Israelites had seen God's power at the Red Sea, they began to complain. There was no good water to drink. And soon they had eaten all the bread they had brought out of Egypt. "Why did you bring us out here to die?" they complained to Moses and Aaron.

Moses knew that the people were really complaining against God. So Moses asked God what to do. Once again God took care of the people. God gave them water to drink and sent manna and quails for them to eat. God continued to provide food and water for the Israelites in the wilderness for forty years, until they reached …

The Promised Land.

| God Promises Abraham a New Land | Isaac | Jacob | Joseph | Abraham's Descendants in Egypt | Moses in Egypt | Moses in Midian | God Calls Moses | Plagues in Egypt | The Passover |

If you obey my voice and keep my covenant, you shall be my treasured possession out of all the peoples.

(Exodus 19:5*a*)

Did You Know?

Mt. Sinai, where God gave the Ten Commandments, is the same mountain that was called Mt. Horeb when Moses first heard God's call. When God first called to Moses from the burning bush, God said, "This shall be a sign for you that it is I who sent you: when you have brought the people out of Egypt, you shall worship God on this mountain."

LMTOANOETHOHMEUIOSIM

The first of the Ten Commandments reminded God's people that they must worship only the one true God—even though the people around them worshiped many gods. Follow the lines from each of the letters in the phrase "only one God" to discover what the belief in only one God is called today. Write the letters in order on the line to see the word.

1200 B.C.

| God Frees the Israelites | Surviving the Wilderness | **Ten Commandments** | Worship in the Wilderness | Moses Sees the Promised Land | Joshua Leads God's People | The Covenant Is Renewed | Living in the Promised Land |

When Moses arrived at Mt. Sinai with the Israelites, it was a place he had been before. Read God's promise to Moses in Exodus 3:12. Then read the signing to learn the two names given in the Bible for the same mountain.

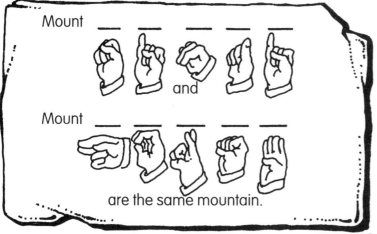

Mount _____ _____ _____ _____ _____

and

Mount _____ _____ _____ _____ _____

are the same mountain.

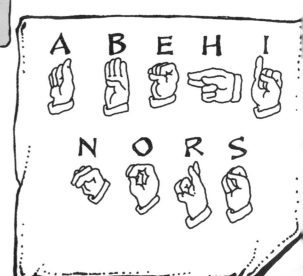

A B E H I

N O R S

Across

3. Mountain where Jesus went to pray after the last Passover meal with his disciples. (Luke 22:39)
4. Mountain where Noah's ark came to rest. (Genesis 8:1-4)
5. Mountain from which Moses saw The Promised Land. (Deuteronomy 34:1-4)

Down

1. Mountain of the Lord, where God called to Moses from a burning bush. (Exodus 3:1)
2. Mountain where Moses received the tablets of the Ten Commandments. (Exodus 34:29, 32)
3. Mountain on which Solomon built a Temple for God. (2 Chronicles 3:1)

After three months the people came to the wilderness of Sinai, where they camped at the foot of the mountain. Moses knew that they were at the holy mountain of God, so he was not surprised when God called to him. God told Moses to tell the people to prepare to hear God in three days.

Three days later the mountain shook and trembled. There was thunder and lightening and trumpet sounds. At the top of the mountain there was a cloud of smoke. Then God spoke the words of the Ten Commandments. The first four commandments would help the people learn to honor God as they continued to journey toward …

The Promised Land.

2000 B.C.	1500 B.C.	1250 B.C.

God Promises Abraham a New Land   Isaac   Jacob   Joseph   Abraham's Descendants in Egypt   Moses in Egypt   Moses in Midian   God Calls Moses   Plagues in Egypt   The Passover

All the words that the LORD has spoken we will do.

(Exodus 24:3b)

Did You Know?

The Ten Commandments had to be written twice. When the people thought Moses had spent too much time on the mountain, they decided to make another god of their own. So Aaron helped them to make a god in the shape of a calf from their gold rings. When Moses saw the golden calf, he became angry and threw down the tablets on which God had written the Ten Commandments. The tablets broke into pieces at Moses' feet. Later Moses went back to the mountain where God spoke the Ten Commandments again and had Moses write them on new stones.

1. Worship only God.
2. Do not make or worship idols.
3. Use God's name with respect.
4. Keep the Sabbath day holy.
5. Honor your father and mother.
6. Do not murder.
7. Be faithful in marriage.
8. Do not take what is not yours.
9. Always tell the truth.
10. Be satisfied with the things that you possess.

Read the Ten Commandments from Exodus 20:1-17. Compare the list in the picture with the list in the Bible. Do you understand what each one means?

Copy each of the Ten Commandments (from your Bible or from the list pictured) onto a separate index card. Then use the cards to play these games.

1. Separate the four commandments about loving God and the six commandments about loving others into two separate stacks.
2. Arrange the commandments in the order they are printed in Exodus 20:1-17.
3. Have a friend remove one of the cards; then decide which commandment is missing.

1200 B.C.

| God Frees the Israelites | Surviving the Wilderness | Ten Commandments | Worship in the Wilderness | Moses Sees the Promised Land | Joshua Leads God's People | The Covenant Is Renewed | Living in the Promised Land |

Follow the spiral, choosing every other letter along the way. When you reach the end, you will have discovered what Jesus said when asked about God's commandments. (Matthew 22:37)

Jesus said,

"_____ "

Jesus added a second commandment that was also part of the law the people knew from the days of Moses. Untangle the strings to find Jesus words that he had learned from Leviticus 19:18.

"_____ "

Before Moses left the mountain, God gave the people six more commandments. These commandments would help the people know how to live together in peace as God wanted them to live. God knew that the people would need guidance as they continued to travel through the wilderness. And God knew that knowing how to relate to one another would be an important skill if they wanted to live as God's people in …

The Promised Land.

2000 B.C.	1500 B.C.	1250 B.C.

God Promises Abraham a New Land	Isaac	Jacob	Joseph	Abraham's Descendants in Egypt	Moses in Egypt	Moses in Midian	God Calls Moses	Plagues in Egypt	The Passover

The glory of the LORD filled the Tabernacle.

(Exodus 40:34)

Did You Know?

The tablets on which the Ten Commandments were written were kept in the ark of the covenant in the Tabernacle. There was also an urn of manna and Aaron's rod. No one knows what eventually happened to the ark of the covenant and its contents. We only know that later in the Bible story, they had been lost.

acacia
altar
ark
basins
bells
cherubim
curtains
diadem
ephod
firepans
fork
grating
incense
lampstand
leather
oil
onyx

pegs
pillars
poles
pots
robes
screens
shovels
snuffers
tabernacle
table
tent
trays
tunic
turban
vestment

```
T R A Y S M O S E S V C E N S T E
U A I N C E N S E B E L L S R I R
R O B E N N A A R O S U M P E G S
B M R E E L I N D A T K R O F L P
A C H E R U B I M A M M O C F L O
N E R X Y N O T F I E J B O U E L
D C F O D I A D E M N O E B N R E
S O R S S B R C U R T A I N S O S
Z A G P L U K B L A M P S T A N D
F I R E P A N S L E I H S U L S V
S U A C A C I A L I O E C T T H D
I M T E N T P R S V S N I S A B O
X P I L L A R S E O W T N E R A H
T O N X O B C L C H I L U D R E P
Y B G P O T S Y L L E A T H E R E
```

God gave detailed instructions for building the tabernacle and its contents. Find the words that describe the tabernacle in the letters.

If you want a challenge, cover the word list and find the words by reading chapters 36-39 of the Book of Exodus!

Did you find some other familiar words?

1200 B.C.

| God Frees the Israelites | Surviving the Wilderness | Ten Commandments | **Worship in the Wilderness** | Moses Sees the Promised Land | Joshua Leads God's People | The Covenant Is Renewed | Living in the Promised Land |

The ark of the covenant was a sign of God's presence. What other signs of God's presence do we hear about in the stories of the Bible?

Cover the graph with a blank sheet of paper. Then slide the paper slowly to the right until you reach a marker ☺. That will be the first letter of the first sign. Continue sliding the paper until you have spelled out five signs of God's presence.

To check your answers in your Bible, read Genesis 9:16, Genesis 28:10-16, Exodus 10:35, Exodus 13:21, and Exodus 16:14-15, 31.

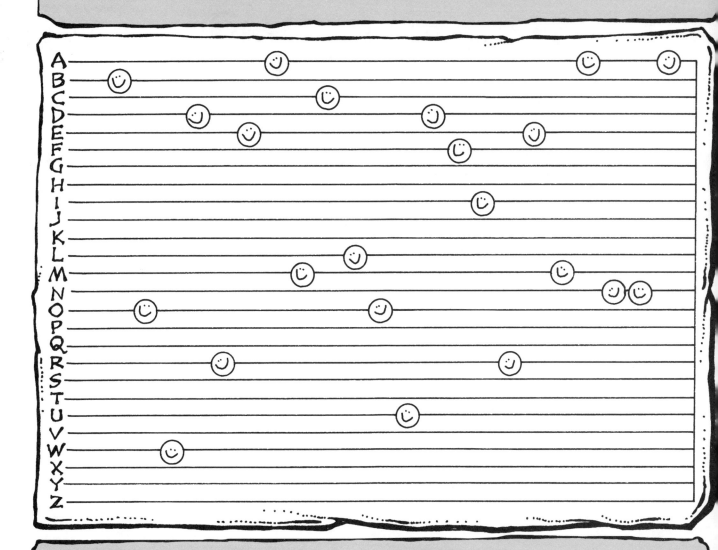

On the mountain God gave Moses instructions for building a tabernacle, a portable "tent of meeting." There God could dwell among the people as they journeyed through the wilderness. Now the people understood why God had told them to ask their Egyptian neighbors for silver and gold before they left Egypt. They brought their riches so that the tabernacle could be built according to God's instructions. In fact, they brought so much that the builders had to ask them to stop!

The stone tablets on which the Ten Commandments were written were put in the ark of the covenant inside the Tabernacle. God would continue to meet with Moses in the Tabernacle as the Israelites continued their journey to …

The Promised Land.

2000 B.C. — 1500 B.C. — 1250 B.C.

| God Promises Abraham a New Land | Isaac | Jacob | Joseph | Abraham's Descendants in Egypt | Moses in Egypt | Moses in Midian | God Calls Moses | Plagues in Egypt | The Passover |

Did You Know?

Soon after leaving Egypt, Moses sent spies into Canaan. They came back to tell about the richness and beauty of the land. But ten of the twelve spies were afraid of the people they had seen in Canaan. Caleb and Joshua were the only two who said, "God will help us take the land." But the people were afraid and rebelled against God again. God forgave them, but they were forced to wander in the wilderness for forty years before there was another chance to enter The Promised Land.

The LORD said to him [Moses], "This is the land of which I swore to Abraham, to Isaac, and to Jacob."

(Deuteronomy 34:4a)

Moses' life is divided into three major periods of forty years each in Acts 7:20-36. Illustrate the major events in Moses' life here.

From birth to 40 years old.	From 40 years old to 80 years old	From 80 years old to 120 years old

Moses Is Born — Moses Grows Up in Egypt — Moses Flees to Midian — Moses Becomes a Shepherd in Midian — Moses Hears God's Call — Moses and the Israelites wander in the Wilderness — Moses Dies

1200 B.C.

| God Frees the Israelites | Surviving the Wilderness | Ten Commandments | Worship in the Wilderness | Moses Sees the Promised Land | Joshua Leads God's People | The Covenant Is Renewed | Living in the Promised Land |

From the top of Mt. Nebo, Moses looked out over the land that had been promised to Abraham. Imagine that you are Moses, standing on the top of the mountain. Write the name of each tribe in the area Moses assigned for it to occupy. The areas are identified with letters.

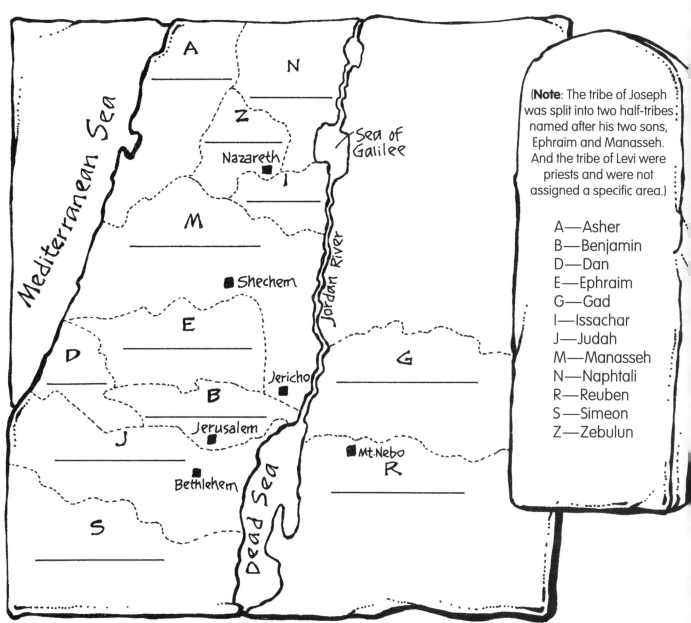

(**Note**: The tribe of Joseph was split into two half-tribes named after his two sons, Ephraim and Manasseh. And the tribe of Levi were priests and were not assigned a specific area.)

A—Asher
B—Benjamin
D—Dan
E—Ephraim
G—Gad
I—Issachar
J—Judah
M—Manasseh
N—Naphtali
R—Reuben
S—Simeon
Z—Zebulun

After many years of wandering in the wilderness, the Israelites finally reached the borders of Canaan—the land that had been promised to Abraham and Abraham's descendants. God showed Moses the whole land of Canaan from the top of Mt. Nebo. But God said to Moses, "I have let you see it with your eyes, but you shall not cross over there."

Then Moses died. The Israelites mourned for their leader Moses. But they were comforted by the blessing that Moses had given them before his death. They were strengthened because Moses had assured them that they would soon enter …

The Promised Land.

2000 B.C. ———————————————————— 1500 B.C. ———————————————————— 1250 B.C.

| God Promises Abraham a New Land | Isaac | Jacob | Joseph | Abraham's Descendants in Egypt | Moses in Egypt | Moses in Midian | God Calls Moses | Plagues in Egypt | The Passover |

The LORD spoke to Joshua ... "Proceed to cross the Jordan, ... into the land that I am giving to them, to the Israelites."

(Joshua 1:2)

Did You Know?
Caleb and Joshua, the spies who had tried to get the people to trust God and occupy Canaan many years earlier, were the only two of the Israelites who had left Egypt with Moses who lived to enter The Promised Land. All of the others died because of their unfaithfulness, but their children were allowed to enter The Promised Land.

Name That Tribe!

Remember that Jacob had twelve sons. When the people of Israel were organized into tribes, there were twelve tribes. Each tribe was named for one of the sons of Jacob.

The tribe of Joseph was represented by two half-tribes because Jacob gave his favorite son a double portion of the land (Genesis 48:22). The half-tribes of Joseph were named for Joseph's two sons.

Find the names of the twelve tribes of Israel in the faces of Jacob's sons and grandsons.

1200 B.C.

| God Frees the Israelites | Surviving the Wilderness | Ten Commandments | Worship in the Wilderness | Moses Sees the Promised Land | Joshua Leads God's People | The Covenant Is Renewed | Living in the Promised Lan |

Write the names of the twelve tribes on the stones taken from the Jordan River to become a reminder of God's action.

God chose Joshua to be the new leader of the Israelites. After three days, Joshua gave God's instructions to the people: "Priests, carry the ark of the covenant into the river and stand there." The people watched with amazement as God rolled the waters back. The priests walked out into the center of the river on dry land!

When all the people had crossed the river, Joshua said, "Choose twelve stones from the center of the river, one for each of the tribes of Israel." When the stones were gathered, the priests came out of the river. As soon as their feet touched dry land, the waters of the river rolled back into place.

Following Joshua's instructions, the people of Israel built a memorial with the twelve stones. Today when their children ask, "What do these stones mean?" they tell them about the day that God dried up the Jordan River—just as God had done for the Israelite slaves at the Red Sea—so that they could cross over into …

The Promised Land.

2000 B.C.	1500 B.C.	1250 B.C.

God Promises Abraham a New Land	Isaac	Jacob	Joseph	Abraham's Descendants in Egypt	Moses in Egypt	Moses in Midian	God Calls Moses	Plagues in Egypt	The Passover

Choose this day whom you will serve. (Joshua 24:15a)

Did You Know?
Jesus said something similar to what Joshua told the people. Jesus said, "No one can serve two masters" (Matthew 6:24). Joshua and Jesus were talking to people in very different circumstances, but each of them knew that people must make a choice in order to serve God.

Joshua knew that it would not be easy for the Israelites to leave behind the gods they had seen the Egyptians worship. Joshua knew that the people must make a choice to serve God or they would fall back into their old ways.

Write a brief letter to God. Tell God what choices you will make to help you serve God. If there are things about your way of living that you need to change, tell God what you will choose to do.

1200 B.C.

God Frees the Israelites | Surviving the Wilderness | Ten Commandments | Worship in the Wilderness | Moses Sees the Promised Land | Joshua Leads God's People | **The Covenant Is Renewed** | Living in the Promised Land

Choosing to serve God means that you will make all of your choices based on what you know God wants you to do.

Use the code to complete a list of questions to ask when you need help to choose the faithful way.

1 Whom will my decision _____ directly? _____?

2 How will those who are affected by my decision ____ ?

3 Will my decision ____ me?

4 Will my decision hurt _____ ?

5 Will I break a ____ if I make this decision?

6 Who is someone I can _____ this situation with before I make a decision?

7 Will my decision make me feel _____ or will it make me feel _____ ?

8 What decision do I think ____ would want me to make?

Remember: Whatever decision you have to make, ask God to be with you.

Joshua was clear about his decision to serve and obey God. Once the people had arrived in Canaan, Joshua reminded them that they must put away the gods that they had learned about in Egypt. And they must resist the temptation to worship the gods of the pagan people in the land that God had given them. They must choose whom they would serve. And the people said: "The Lord our God we will serve, and him we will obey" (Joshua 24:24). Joshua helped the people of Israel renew their covenant with God that day in …

The Promised Land.

2000 B.C. ———————————————— 1500 B.C. ———————————————— 1250 B.C.

| God Promises Abraham a New Land | Isaac | Jacob | Joseph | Abraham's Descendants in Egypt | Moses in Egypt | Moses in Midian | God Calls Moses | Plagues in Egypt | The Passover |

By faith ... Abraham set out, not knowing where he was going.

(Hebrews 11:8)

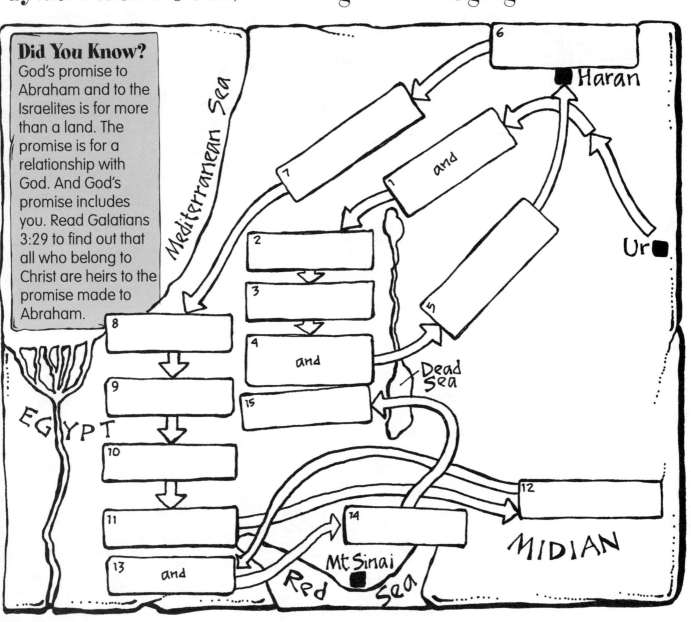

Did You Know?
God's promise to Abraham and to the Israelites is for more than a land. The promise is for a relationship with God. And God's promise includes you. Read Galatians 3:29 to find out that all who belong to Christ are heirs to the promise made to Abraham.

Trace the story of The Promised Land on the map. Begin with God's call to Abraham in Haran.

God called _____ and his wife _____(1) to go to a new land called _____(2). After many years, they had a son whom they named _____(3). He became the father of twin sons—_____ and _____(4).

The younger twin, _____(5), cheated his brother then fled to Haran. He had twelve sons and one daughter. But his son, _____(6), was his favorite. As Jacob and his family returned to Canaan, God changed Jacob's name to _____(7).

1200 B.C.

| God Frees the Israelites | Surviving the Wilderness | Ten Commandments | Worship in the Wilderness | Moses Sees the Promised Land | Joshua Leads God's People | The Covenant Is Renewed | Living in the Promised Land |

Jacob's favorite son, _____(8), was sold by his brothers and taken to Egypt as a slave. In Egypt, he rose to a position of great power. During a famine, Joseph's entire family moved to Egypt and settled in the land of _____(9). After many years, the Hebrews became slaves.

By this time the Hebrews were also called _____(10). _____(11), a Hebrew born in Egypt, was adopted by Pharaoh's daughter. Later he fled from Egypt and settled in Midian. There he heard God call to him from a _____(12). _____ and his brother _____(13) returned to Egypt to get Pharaoh to let God's people go. When the slaves were finally out of Egypt, Moses led them to Mt. Sinai, where God gave them the _____(14).

Finally, the Israelites arrived in Canaan, which is also known as _____(15).

A family tree.

Abraham — Sarah
Isaac — Rebekah
Jacob — Esau

Reuben, Levi, Dan, Gad, Issachar, Dinah, Benjamin
Simeon, Judah, Naphtali, Asher, Zebulon, Joseph
Moses, Caleb, Ephraim, Manasseh
David, Joshua
Jesus

More than four thousand years ago, God made a covenant with Abraham. Abraham would leave his home in Haran and travel to a new land; God would make Abraham's descendants into a great nation who would live in the new land God promised. God's promise was repeated through each generation of Abraham's descendants until the Israelites finally returned to Canaan to live in ...

The Promised Land.

The Answers

God Promises Abraham a New Land

IØÍ WIØÍLL MAØÍKEØÍ OØÍF YOØÍUØÍ AØÍ GREØÍTAØÍT NAØÍTIØÍTOØÍN, AØÍND IØÍ WIØÍLL BLEØÍSS YOØÍUØÍ, AØÍND MAØÍKEØÍ YOØÍUØÍR NAØÍMEØÍ GREØÍTAØÍT, SOØÍ THAØÍT YOØÍUØÍ WIØÍLL BEØÍ AØÍ BLEØÍSSIØÍNG... IØÍ WIØÍLL EØÍSTAØÍBLIØÍSH MY COØÍVEØÍNAØÍNT BEØÍTWEØÍTEØÍN MEØÍ AØÍND YOØÍUØÍ, AØÍND YOØÍUØÍROØÍFFSPRIØÍNG AØÍFTEØÍR YOØÍUØÍ.

Genesis 12:2; 17:7

I WILL MAKE OF YOU A GREAT NATION AND I WILL BLESS YOU AND MAKE YOUR NAME GREAT SO THAT YOU WILL BE A BLESSING . . . I WILL ESTABLISH MY COVENANT BETWEEN ME AND YOU, AND YOUR OFFSPRING AFTER YOU.

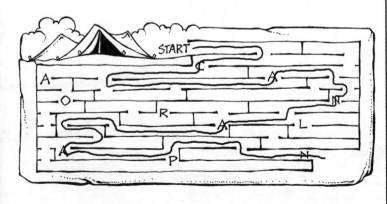

The Promised Land is called CANAAN .

Isaac

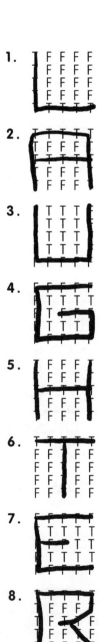

1.
2.
3.
4.
5.
6.
7.
8.

Isaac means LAUGHTER

Jacob

Abraham (Genesis 17:5) — laughter

Sarah (Genesis 17:15) — the hairy one, also nicknamed Red

Isaac (Genesis 21:6) — one who strives with God

Esau (Genesis 25:25, 30) — princess

Jacob (Genesis 25:26) — ancestor of many nations

Israel (Genesis 32:28) — one who takes another by the heel

```
L   BX  OHR  AZCD  OHR  GZD  ZF
I   AM  THE  LORD,  THE  GOD  OF

B  J  C  B  H  B  X   B  N  D   O  H  R   G  Z  D   Z  F
A B R A H A M   A N D   T H E   G O D   O F

L  S  B  B  Q   O  H  R   A  B  N  D   Z  N   W  H  L  Q  H
I S A A C;   T H E   L A N D   O N   W H I C H

Y  Z  U   A  L  R   L   W  L  A  A   G  L  V  R   O  Z   Y  Z  U
Y O U   L I E   I   W I L L   G I V E   T O   Y O U

B  N  D   O  Z   Y  Z  U  C   Z  F  F  S   P  C  L  N  G
A N D   T O   Y O U R   O F F S P R I N G...

K  N  Z  W   O  H  B  O   L   W  L  A  A   J  C  L  N  G
K N O W   T H A T   I...   W I L L   B R I N G

Y  Z  U   J  B  Q  K   O  Z   O  H  L  S   A  B  N  D
Y O U   B A C K   T O   T H I S   L A N D.
```

Joseph

```
A  U  J  L  N  B  E  N  J  A  L  D
N  E  O  L  E  J  P  H  I  O  S  I
A  S  S  U  N  Z  O  V  O  S  E  L
D  A  E  S  M  A  E  O  R  M  E  A
J  O  E  V  I  L  U  B  E  P  H  T
P  E  H  J  A  M  I  N  U  E  P  H
N  I  M  A  J  N  E  B  B  L  E  P
D  D  I  N  A  H  J  O  E  L  U  A
J  A  I  S  S  A  M  N  R  H  N
D  G  A  C  H  A  H  D  R  A  M  N
B  E  N  J  J  O  S  E  U  O  D  Z
I  S  S  A  C  H  A  R  R  J  O  S
```

Abraham's Descendants in Egypt

A B C D E G H I J K L M N O P Q R S T U V W X Y Z   __F__

B C D E F G H I J K L M N O P Q R S T U V W X Y Z   __A__

A B C D E F G H I J K L N O P Q R S T U V W X Y Z   __M__

A B C D E F G H J K L M N O P Q R S T U V W X Y Z   __I__

A B C D E F G H I J K L M O P Q R S T U V W X Y Z   __N__

A B C D F G H I J K L M N O P Q R S T U V W X Y Z   __E__

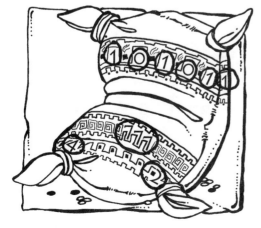

How many children were born to Joseph in Egypt? __2__ (Genesis 46:27)

How many members of Jacob's family came into Egypt? __70__ (Genesis 46:27)

How many years did Jacob, now called Israel, live in Egypt? __17__ (Genesis 47:27-28)

How old was Jacob when he died? __147__ (Genesis 47:27-28)

How long did Joseph live? __110__ (Genesis 50:22)

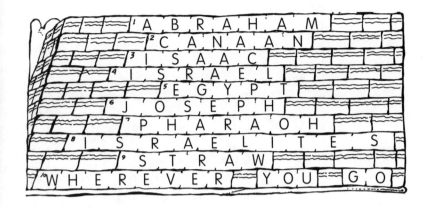

1. ABRAHAM
2. CANAAN
3. ISAAC
4. ISRAEL
5. EGYPT
6. JOSEPH
7. PHARAOH
8. ISRAELITES
9. STRAW
10. WHEREVER YOU GO

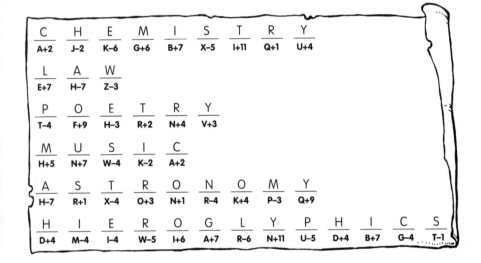

C	H	E	M	I	S	T	R	Y
A+2	J–2	K–6	G+6	B+7	X–5	I+11	Q+1	U+4

L	A	W
E+7	H–7	Z–3

P	O	E	T	R	Y
T–4	F+9	H–3	R+2	N+4	V+3

M	U	S	I	C
H+5	N+7	W–4	K–2	A+2

A	S	T	R	O	N	O	M	Y
H–7	R+1	X–4	O+3	N+1	R–4	K+4	P–3	Q+9

H	I	E	R	O	G	L	Y	P	H	I	C	S
D+4	M–4	I–4	W–5	I+6	A+7	R–6	N+11	U–5	D+4	B+7	G–4	T–1

Moses in Egypt

- C 1. — A. to fly
- D 2. — B. Loaded boat
- G 3. — C. Tree
- B 4. — D. To see
- I 5. — E. Dew, rain
- E 6. — F. Night
- F 7. — G. To walk
- J 8. — H. Moon, month
- H 9. — I. Water
- A 10. — J. Agricultural land

```
H S P R I M I R D
S P H U A Z 'S D
D A A I J O C H
H A R O P P I Z
M I A M R R J 'S
M O O M I R A D
S S H I P U A H
E R 'S D A U G H
B E D U G T E R
J O C H E B E D
P H T P H A R A
B E E D M I R I
R R O P P I Z 'S
```

Moses in Midian

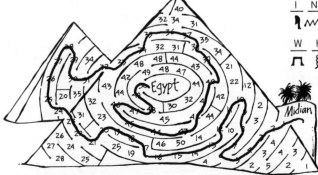

A B C D E F G H I J K L M N O P Q R S T U V W X Y Z

WHEN I AM AFRAID,

I PUT MY TRUST IN YOU.

IN GOD,

WHOSE WORD I PRAISE.

God Calls Moses

Separate the letters around the edge of the burning bush to find Moses' excuses for not doing what God wanted and the ways God promised to help. The lower case letters are Moses' excuses. The capital letters are God's promises. (Check your answers by reading Exodus 4:1, 10-15.)

But suppose they do not believe me or listen to me? I have never been eloquent. I am slow of speech and slow of tongue.

WHO GIVES SPEECH TO MORTALS? IS IT NOT I THE LORD? NOW GO AND I WILL BE WITH YOUR MOUTH AND TEACH YOU WHAT YOU ARE TO SPEAK.

O my Lord please send someone else.

WHAT OF YOUR BROTHER AARON THE LEVITE? I KNOW THAT HE CAN SPEAK FLUENTLY. EVEN NOW HE IS COMING OUT TO MEET YOU AND WHEN HE SEES YOU HIS HEART WILL BE GLAD. I WILL BE WITH YOUR MOUTH AND WITH HIS MOUTH AND WILL TEACH YOU WHAT YOU SHALL DO.

Plagues in Egypt

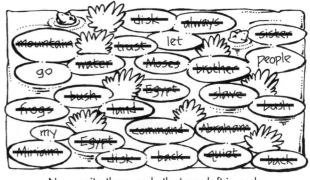

Now write the words that are left in order to find God's message to Pharaoh.

LET MY PEOPLE GO

LBODO ___BLOOD___ — Exodus 10:13-14
RGFSO ___FROGS___ — Exodus 9:2-3
SGATN ___GNATS___ — Exodus 12:29
LFSEI ___FLIES___ — Exodus 7:20-21
CLESTEPENI ___PESTILENCE___ — Exodus 8:17
LBSOI ___BOILS___ — Exodus 10:22
HLIA ___HAIL___ — Exodus 8:5-6
TUOLCSS ___LOCUSTS___ — Exodus 8:21-24
RADNKSES ___DARKNESS___ — Exodus 9:22-26
HETDA ___DEATH___ — Exodus 9:10

The Passover

God told Moses that the night of the last plague would be remembered and celebrated as the ___FIRST___ month of the year for Hebrews. (Exodus 12:2)

On that night the blood of a lamb was to be put on the two ___DOORPOSTS___ and lintel of the houses of the Israelites. (Exodus 12:7) Then the people in the house would share a meal of roasted ___LAMB___, ___UNLEAVENED___ bread, and bitter ___HERBS___. (Exodus 12:8)

When the Lord passed over the houses of Israelites, the blood on the houses would be a ___SIGN___, and no plague would destroy the people of Israel. (Exodus 12:13)

The Lord said that this day would be a day of ___REMEMBRANCE___ for the Israelites. (Exodus 12:14) It would be a day when they recall that God had passed over their houses on the night that the ___FIRSTBORN___ of all others in the land of Egypt were destroyed. (Exodus 12:12)

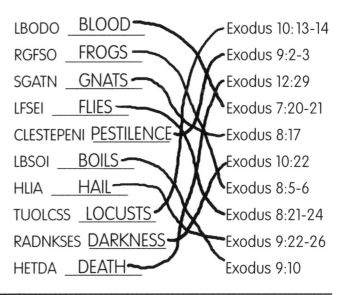

Color the path that completes each maze from beginning to end to find the word that describes the Israelites exit from Egypt.

Find the book in your Bible that tells about the slaves leaving Egypt.

It is the Book of E X O D U S.

START AT ★...END AT ●

God kept the promise to be with the Israelites wherever they went. Use the code to find out how the people knew that God was with them when they left Egypt.

The Lord went in front of them in a pillar of C L O U D by day

...and in a pillar of F I R E by night. (Exodus 13:21-22)

Moses' sister, Miriam, sang with joy. She sang:

S I N G   T O   T H E   L O R D
F O R   H E   H A S   T R I U M P H E D
G L O R I O U S L Y

A	♩	J	♪	R	○
B	♩	K	♪	S	♩
C	♩	L	♫	T	♩
D	♩	M	♫	U	♪
E	♩	N	♩	V	♩
F	♫	O	♩	W	♩
G	♩	P	♩	X	♩
H	○	Q	♩	Y	♪
I	♪			Z	♫

WORK
WOR**D**
W**A**R**D**
LAR**D**
LAND

KILL
MILL
MILE
MALE
SALE
SAVE

DRINK
DRANK
PRANK
PLANK
PLANE
PLACE

The first of the Ten Commandments reminded God's people that they must worship only the one true God—even though the people around them worshiped many gods. Follow the lines from each of the letters in the phrase "only one God" to discover what the belief in only one God is called today. Write the letters in order on the line to see the word.

MONOTHEISM

Crossword:
3. MOUNTOFOLIVES
4. ARARAT
5. NEBO
1. HOREB (down)
2. SINAI (down)
3. MORIAH (down)

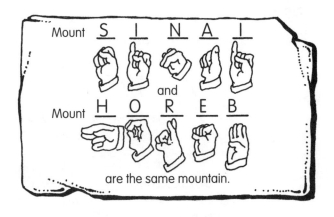

Mount S I N A I

and

Mount H O R E B

are the same mountain.

Ten Commandments 2

Follow the spiral, choosing every other letter along the way. When you reach the end, you will have discovered what Jesus said when asked about God's commandments. (Matthew 22:37)

Jesus said,

"You shall love the Lord your God with all your heart, and with all your soul and with all your mind"

Jesus added a second commandment that was also part of the law the people knew from the days of Moses. Untangle the strings to find Jesus words that he had learned from Leviticus 19:18.

"Love your neighbor as yourself."

Worship in the Wilderness

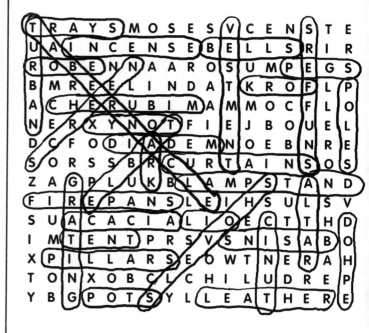

Moses Sees the Promised Land

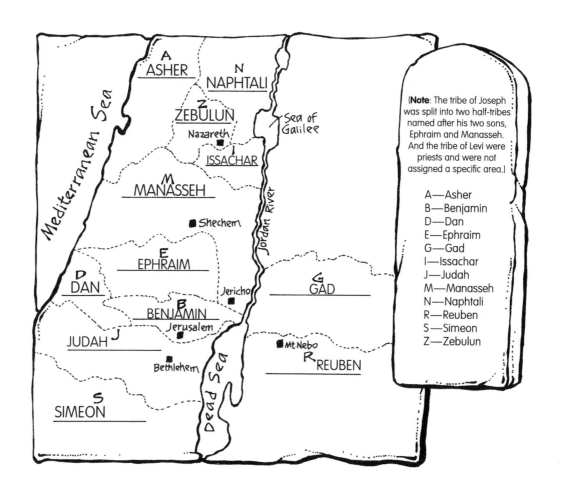

(Note: The tribe of Joseph was split into two half-tribes named after his two sons, Ephraim and Manasseh. And the tribe of Levi were priests and were not assigned a specific area.)

A—Asher
B—Benjamin
D—Dan
E—Ephraim
G—Gad
I—Issachar
J—Judah
M—Manasseh
N—Naphtali
R—Reuben
S—Simeon
Z—Zebulun

Joshua Leads God's People

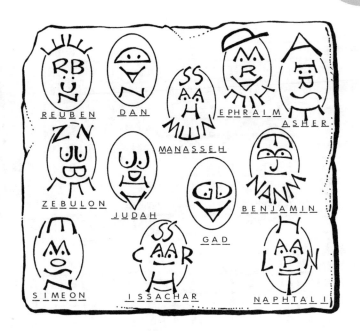

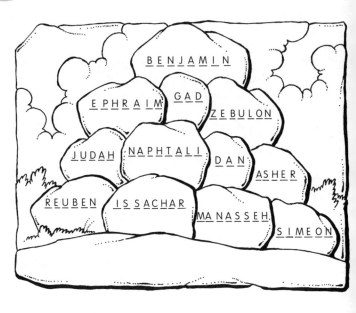

The Covenant Is Renewed

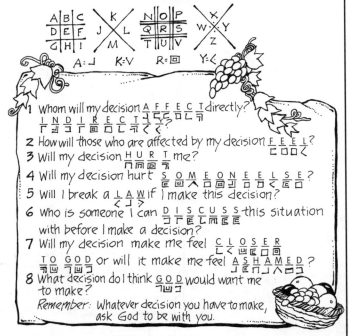

1 Whom will my decision A F F E C T directly? I N D I R E C T L Y?
2 How will those who are affected by my decision F E E L?
3 Will my decision H U R T me?
4 Will my decision hurt S O M E O N E E L S E?
5 Will I break a L A W if I make this decision?
6 Who is someone I can D I S C U S S this situation with before I make a decision?
7 Will my decision make me feel C L O S E R T O G O D or will it make me feel A S H A M E D?
8 What decision do I think G O D would want me to make?

Remember: Whatever decision you have to make, ask God to be with you.

Living in the Promised Land

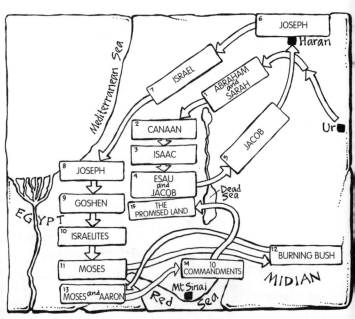